How to use this book

Follow the advice, in italics, given for you on each page.
Support the children as they read the text that is shaded in cream.
Praise *the children at every step!*

Detailed guidance is provided in the Read Write Inc. Phonics Handbook

9 reading activities

Children:
Practise reading the speed sounds.
Read the green, red and challenge words for the story.
Listen as you read the introduction.
Discuss the vocabulary check with you.
Read the story.
Re-read the story and discuss the 'questions to talk about'.
Read the story with fluency and expression.
Answer the questions to 'read and answer'.
Practise reading the speed words.

Speed sounds

Consonants *Say the pure sounds (do not add 'uh').*

f ff	l ll (le)	m mm	n nn kn	r (rr)	s ss	v (ve)	z zz s	sh	th	ng nk

b bb	c k ck	d dd	g gg	h	j	p (pp)	qu	t tt	w (wh)	x	y	ch tch

Vowels *Say the sounds in and out of order.*

at	hen head	in	on	up	day	see happy	high find	blow no

zoo	look	car	for door snore	fair	whirl	shout	boy spoil

*Each box contains one sound but sometimes more than one grapheme. Focus graphemes are **circled**.*

Green words

ri<u>ch</u>   <u>which</u>   stro<u>ng</u>   h<u>ea</u>d   <u>ou</u>t   li<u>tt</u> <u>le</u>   told   don't

h<u>oo</u>d   st<u>oo</u>d   cr<u>oo</u>k   g<u>oo</u>d   br<u>oo</u>k   <u>sh</u> <u>oo</u>k   t<u>oo</u>k   f<u>oo</u>t

---

Read in syllables.

Rob`in  →  Robin        a`<u>rr</u> <u>ow</u> → a<u>rr</u> <u>ow</u>   con`test → contest

him`self  →  himself        w<u>oo</u>d`en → w<u>oo</u>den

Read the root word first and then with the ending.

gi<u>ve</u> → givi<u>ng</u>   rob → ro<u>bb</u>i<u>ng</u>

li<u>ve</u> → livi<u>ng</u> → lived   happen → happened

gasp → gasped   <u>wh</u>a<u>ck</u> → <u>wh</u>a<u>ck</u>ed

w<u>oo</u>d → w<u>oo</u>ds   r<u>oo</u>k → r<u>oo</u>ks

h<u>oo</u>k → h<u>oo</u>ked   c<u>oo</u>k → c<u>oo</u>ked

<u>oo</u>k → l<u>oo</u>ki<u>ng</u>

Red words

your who ta<u>ll</u> <u>you</u> of to want th<u>ey</u>

be me he s<u>ai</u>d my by ca<u>ll</u> a<u>ll</u> o<u>ne</u> so was <u>are</u>

Challenge words

Jo<u>hn</u>   bri<u>dge</u>   stren<u>gth</u>   riv<u>er</u>

Robin Hood

Introduction

Do you know the legend of Robin Hood?
Many people said that he was a real person who lived a
long time ago. He was famous for having a gang of friends -
called the Merry Men - and for taking things from the rich
to give to the poor. Do you think that's a good idea?

One day he meets a man called John Little (who is actually
really big). He challenges John to a friendly fight.

Who do you think will win?

Story written by Gill Munton
Illustrated by Tim Archbold

Vocabulary check

Discuss the meaning (as used in the story) after the children have read each word.

	definition:	sentence:
band of Merry Men	Robin Hood's gang	Robin Hood lived in the woods with his band of Merry Men.
crook	a robber	To the rich he was a crook ...
brags	shows off	John Little brags that he can win...
contest	a fight	a contest with Robin Hood.
fast-running brook	a little river where water runs very quickly	He stepped on to the wooden bridge which crossed the fast-running brook.
still	not move	Both men stood very still.

Punctuation to note in this story:
1. Capital letters to start sentences and full stops to end sentences
2. Capital letters for names
3. Exclamation marks to show anger, shock and surprise
4. 'Wait and see' dots...

Robin Hood

As the storybooks will tell you,

Robin Hood lived in the woods

with his band of Merry Men,

robbing from the rich and giving to the poor.

To the rich he was a crook,

but to the poor that he helped,

he was a good man.

In this story, a man called John Little

brags that he can win a contest with Robin Hood.

"I am going hunting," Robin said to his Merry Men. "I will not be long."

He stepped on to the wooden bridge which crossed the fast-running brook.

On the bridge he met a man, tall, and strong-looking.
(This was John Little.)

Both men stood very still.

Then Robin said, "Let me get past, will you?"

"I will not," grunted John.

"Then I will shoot an arrow at your chest!"
Robin took an arrow from his belt.

John shook his head.
"I have only a stick in my hand," he said.
"I don't mind having a contest, but you must
put that arrow back and find a stick.
Then I will set upon you, and I will win!"

So Robin cut himself a stick.

He swung it at John Little, and then sprang at him,

hitting John with his stick.

John gasped, and whacked Robin
with all his strength.
Robin fell off the bridge and into
the brook!

Both men began to grin. John stood on the bridge and Robin stood up to his neck in the brook.

John hooked him out by the foot with his stick, and then Robin, wet to the skin, called to his Merry Men.

When Robin told them what had happened,

the Merry Men wanted to push John into the brook.

But Robin said, "A man who can win a contest with me is a good man

to have for a pal.

John Little, you can be

one of my Merry Men,

and as you are so big

and tall, we shall call you

Little John!"

As they went back to the camp,

they shot ten rooks and took ten fish from the brook.

So Robin Hood and all his Merry Men had a very good lunch,

cooked by Little John!

Questions to talk about

Re-read the page. Read the question to the children. Tell them whether it is a **FIND IT** *question or* **PROVE IT** *question.*

FIND IT

✓ Turn to the page

✓ Read the question

✓ Find the answer

PROVE IT

✓ Turn to the page

✓ Read the question

✓ Find your evidence

✓ Explain why

Page 9:	PROVE IT	Why did the rich people hate Robin Hood? Why did the poor people like him?
Page 10:	FIND IT	Who did Robin Hood meet when he crossed the bridge?
Page 11:	PROVE IT	Why did John Little want Robin to put his arrow away and find a stick?
Page 12:	FIND IT	What happened to Robin Hood when John Little pushed him?
Page 13:	PROVE IT	Why did both men laugh when Robin was in the brook?
Page 14:	PROVE IT	What does Robin say to his men when they want to push John Little into the brook?
Page 15:	PROVE IT	What did everyone eat for lunch?

Questions to read and answer

(Children complete without your help.)

1. Where did Robin Hood live?
   Robin Hood lived **in the woods** / a box / a flat.

2. Where did John and Robin meet?
   John met Robin **on a bridge** / in a stream / in a wood.

3. How did John hook Robin out of the brook?
   John hooked Robin out of the brook by **the chest** / foot / hand.

4. Where did the Merry Men want to push John?
   The Merry Men wanted to push John into **the mud** / sand / brook.

5. Who cooked lunch?
   Lunch was cooked by **Robin Hood** / the Merry Men / Little John.

Speed words

Children practise reading the words across the rows, down the columns and in and out of order clearly and quickly.

brook	good	shook	looking	stick
cooking	with	strong	head	hitting
helped	contest	out	all	men
tall	do	call	your	called

18